ILLUSTRATED CLASSIC EDITIONS

STORIES
FROM THE BIBLE
OLD AND NEW TESTAMENT

adapted by
**Mitsu Yamamoto
and Claudia
Vurnakes**

**Illustrations by
Lloyd Birmingham**

**BARONET
B·O·O·K·S**

BARONET BOOKS, New York, New York

ILLUSTRATED CLASSIC EDITIONS

Cover Copyright © MCMXC

Playmore Inc., Publishers and
Waldman Publishing Corp.,
New York, N.Y. All Rights Reserved.

Interior Text and Art Copyright © MCMXC

Waldman Publishing Corp.
New York, New York

BARONET BOOKS is a trademark of Playmore Inc., Publishers
and Waldman Publishing Corp., New York, New York

No part of this book may be reproduced or
copied in any form without written
permission from the publisher.

Printed in Canada

Contents

God Makes the World

Thousands and thousands of years ago there was no earth, no blue sky, no people or animals. God saw there was only water and darkness.

Stretching out His hand, He gave an order to the Spirit that was in Him. God said, "Let light be born." Instantly light flooded all around Him. God was pleased by the light that He made from His own Inner Spirit. He decided: "I will call the light 'Day' and I will call the darkness 'Night.'"

That was God's work on the first day of the world.

On the second and third days He moved His arm over His head in a half-circle and made the sky. Shaking His fingers He threw off clouds as part of the sky. Working quickly, he gathered the water into many places and called these places 'seas.' The earth was made next—to fit between the seas. On earth He made plants, trees and fruits start to grow.

On the fourth day the sun and moon were made. The purpose of the sun was to make the day very bright. Because God wanted the night to be dark, He made the moon a very dim light. But the moon got some help in lighting the night when God made the stars.

The fifth day all the birds and all the fish were made.

On the sixth day God made cows, lions, snakes, spiders and all the other animals and insects. Now He was almost finished in making the world. But there was still one important matter to attend to: a human being.

God picked up a little dust from the

He made plants, trees, and fruits.

ground. This dust was to become Adam. God needed Adam—and the people who would be born after Adam—to take charge of the earth. People would manage all the animals and plants and fruits that God had made in these six days. So He decided to make Adam in his own image.

Adam was born from the dust God had picked up. God gave him a garden to live in, at a place called 'Eden.' In Eden Adam was taught to eat and to take his food from the plants and fruits now on the earth. But one tree was never to be touched, God said. This was the "tree of knowledge."

God had worked for six days. He looked about Him and was pleased by what He had made. So on the seventh day, God rested.

Earth was ready to begin its life.

God gave Adam a garden to live in.

Wild and tame animals lived in peace.

Adam And Eve: The Fall Of Man

The garden of Eden was beautiful. When Adam looked around him, he saw plants in blossom and trees filled with fruit. He could hear the pleasant sound of running water because four rivers flowed through the garden. Wild animals and tame ones lived together in peace. There were big insects and snakes, but Adam was not afraid of them and they were not afraid of Adam.

Adam went about the garden giving everything a name, as God had told him to do. But one tree God had already named: the tree of knowledge. He told Adam to leave this tree alone, because it could cause death.

BIBLE STORIES

God was not completely satisfied with this garden He had made. He had told everything on earth to grow and multiply. So now there were families of plants, birds, fish, and animals—families of everything except man. Adam needed a wife. God did not want Adam to be lonely.

God now made Eve, a woman, who would be Adam's companion. To make Eve, God put Adam into a very deep sleep. Then He took one of Adam's ribs and used it to make Eve. Adam felt no pain and when he woke up, God spoke to him about Eve.

God said, "This is your wife. You will be close to her because she is part of yourself. She is the same flesh and bone as you are." Though Adam and Eve were naked, they were not shy about it. They felt natural and comfortable because God had put them in the garden of Eden that way.

Because Eve was the same flesh and bone as Adam, she, too, was not afraid of any of

God said, 'This is your wife!"

the wild animals or snakes. So when a snake spoke to her, she listened politely.

"Eve," said the snake, "I thought you and Adam were in charge of this garden."

"We are," answered Eve. "God said so."

"Good," said the snake, with a sly smile. "Then tell me what the fruit on the tree of good and evil tastes like."

Eve blushed with annoyance because she had to admit she did not know." I would die from even touching that tree," she explained.

The snake smiled again and said he didn't believe that would happen. "What *will* happen if you eat the fruit," said the snake, "is that you will have the knowledge of good and evil and be as great as God."

This convinced Eve. She picked some fruit from the tree of good and evil and ate it.

Right away knowledge of good and evil came to Adam and Eve. They looked at themselves and realized they were naked. Quickly they took leaves from a nearby fig

She picked some fruit and ate it.

tree and made aprons to wear. Then they hid because they knew God would be angry with them.

God *was* angry, very angry. He found Adam and Eve and asked why they were hiding.

"Because we are naked so we are afraid," Adam said.

God said, "Yes, you are naked. But how did you get realize this. Did it come from the tree of knowledge?"

Adam had to confess that it had, but he blamed Eve. "I only ate the fruit because my wife—whom You gave to me was eating it and she said I should eat it, too."

"But I was tempted by the snake," Eve exclaimed.

God turned to the snake and put a curse on him. He condemned the snake to crawl on his belly in the dust when he moved on the ground. Also from then on the snake would have all women as his enemy and their children would try to smash his head. In turn,

They hid from God.

snakes would hate them and try to strike at their heels.

God's eyes flashed as He pointed His finger at Eve and promised her great pain in childbirth as payment for her sin in the garden. Adam also had to share the blame. God said from then on Adam would have to work hard all his life to get food. This would be much different from the garden where everything grew by itself and was ready for Adam whenever he reached out his hand.

God made clothes of skin so Adam and Eve could cover all their nakedness. For a final punishment, God cast them out of their beautiful garden. They were sent to a land east of Eden. To prevent them from sneaking back in, He put an angel on guard in the garden of Eden.

Paradise was lost.

Paradise was lost.

Cain planted crops and Abel raised animals.

The First Murder

Adam and Eve became parents. They had two boys: first, Cain, and then, Abel. When he became old enough, Cain started to plant crops. He took care of large fields and cut wheat and picked corn when each was ripe. He did the hard work of a farmer.

Abel raised animals instead of crops. He became a shepherd and took care of flocks of sheep. From his work came meat and wool. He worked as hard as Cain because he had to keep the sheep healthy and safe.

At harvest time both young men brought an offering to God. God looked with approval on the new lambs that Abel gave Him. But when Cain presented his gift of his best fruits and vegetables and grains, God looked away. He did not want Cain's offerings because there was something deep in Cain that God did not approve of.

When Cain saw Abel's gift accepted by God but his own rejected, he got angry. Now God blamed Cain for his anger.

God continued with a warning: "Watch out for sin, Cain, which is like a devil waiting to grab you."

But Cain was so angry that he didn't listen to God's warning. He thought about his rejection all the time and remembered how Abel's lambs had been accepted with pleasure. His anger finally centered on his brother, Abel.

One day Cain found Abel alone in a field. Sin seized hold of him. Cain rushed at Abel and killed him!

This was the first murder on earth.

The first murder on earth.

Cain hid after the murder, but God found him and asked where Abel was. Cain pretended not to know. He said to God, "Am I my brother's keeper?"

Now God's anger burst out because the blood of Abel cried to Him from the ground. God cursed Cain and took away his ability to farm. He made Cain an exile forever.

Cain was overcome. He cried and pleaded with God: "My punishment is more than I can bear. Besides, people will try to kill me when they hear what has happened."

"No," said God, "they will not because I shall put a mark on you. It will remind people that terrible revenge will be taken on anyone who touches you, even though you are a killer."

Cain left the home of his birth. He became a wanderer in a country called Nod.

Adam and Eve were left with no children: Abel was dead and Cain was in exile. Eve wanted another child very much. Finally, she had another son: Seth.

"Am I my brother's keeper?"

Noah loved God and tried to follow his ways.

The Flood

By now thousands and thousands of people lived on the earth. This human race had turned out to be violent and greedy and evil. When God looked at earth, He was sorry He had made it.

God decided the people on earth were too wicked to live any longer. Everybody must be drowned!

But then God paused because He remembered one good man and his family. This man loved God and tried to follow His ways in spite of all the evil around him. The man's name was Noah. He had three married sons:

BIBLE STORIES

Shem, Ham and Japheth. God decided to give the human race another chance. He would let Noah and his family live and bring forth a good people, devoted to serving God.

God directed Noah to build a large boat, called an ark. Following God's directions exactly, Noah made the ark of cypress wood and strong reeds. He covered the outside with tar to make it waterproof. The ark was three stories high, with a door on one side.

When the ark was ready, God told Noah to store food on board, enough to last a long time. Finally God gave Noah the passenger list: Noah and his wife, his three sons and their wives, plus a male and female of every kind of living thing. The animals, even the insects, would come on board the ark in pairs.

When the passengers were on board, Noah closed the door of the ark tightly. It began to rain. It poured rain for 40 days and 40 nights. Little by little all the water raised the ark from the ground. Soon it was float-

God directed Noah to build a large boat.

ing. By now all flat land was under water. Finally even the tops of mountains disappeared in the rising water. Everything and everybody on earth was dead except for the people, animals, birds and other living creatures on the ark.

The ark floated on the flood waters for 150 days. Then God decided it was time to dry the earth so the ark could land. He sent a hot wind and gradually the water level went down. Noah could see only water all around him, but he knew God had promised to bring the ark to dry land.

Luckily there were birds on board. Noah sent out a raven and then a dove to search for dry land. The second trip the dove made, it brought back an olive leaf. Noah waited another week and sent the dove out again. This time the dove didn't return so Noah knew it had found dry land and started to make its new home.

God floated Noah's ark to the mountain of

The dove brought back an olive leaf.

Ararat and told him and the others their journey was over. As they had gone into the ark—side by side—each pair of animals, birds, insects, came onto dry land and went forward to make a new world.

The first thing Noah did was make an altar, with offerings of thanks to God. This deed was so pleasing to God that He made a promise. He said that no matter how wicked people became in the future, He would never destroy the world by flood again. As a reminder of His promise, God made a sign that would would appear in the sky among rain clouds.

This sign can still be seen today: it is a rainbow.

God made a sign in the sky.

They discovered how to make bricks.

Tower of Babel

Noah's family and all the other creatures he had saved came off the ark onto a clean-washed earth. As God wanted, Noah's sons—Shem, Ham and Japheth—started their own families. The years passed, and their families grew; so many, many people were living on the earth.

Finally there were too many people living in one place, and they started to move apart. Some went to a good, flat land called Babel. They settled there and discovered how to make bricks by baking them. With bricks they could make houses, and soon a city rose up.

But the people of Babel worried that they were not famous and well known to people in other lands. They decided to use their bricks to build a tower. A very tall tower would make them famous and bind them together as a people. They decided their tower would reach as high as heaven.

Work started on the tower. As it got taller and taller, God took notice of it. He also heard that the the tower was intended to reach into heaven. This was too bold!

God could easily have stopped the building through force. He could have hurt or killed the Babylonians for making Him angry. Instead God used words.

Since the flood, all men spoke the same language because they came from the same family. God saw that by talking together, people were able to decide things together and work on projects together. He also saw that building the tower would not be the end of the people's boldness. They would go on to

Work started on the tower.

make other selfish plans that would anger God.

God stopped the building of the tower by making people speak different languages. Suddenly they found they didn't understand one another. They couldn't make plans together. One man didn't know what another man wanted so they could no longer work together. They just babbled.

Now, at God's direction, people of one language moved together in one area. Other people who spoke a different language moved away into their own lands. The work on the tower stopped. From then on the tower stood unfinished.

Because God had made people just babble to one another, the tower was known as The Tower of Babel.

People didn't understand one another.

Finally their son, Isaac, was born.

The Sacrifice

Abraham and his wife, Sarah, loved God. They worshipped Him and obeyed Him in all ways. And yet Abraham and Sarah were sad because they had no children and now they were old.

Abraham's obedience to God pleased Him greatly. So God said to Abraham, "Sarah shall bear a child, a son." The two old people could hardly believe this wonderful news but their faith in God was strong. They dared to hope they would be parents.

Finally their son, Isaac, was born: a fine, healthy child. Abraham and Sarah were overjoyed. Isaac grew tall and strong and he, too, followed Abraham in his obedience to God.

One day, God decided to test Abraham. He told Abraham that he must sacrifice his son, his only son, Isaac to him. With the saddest heart Abraham roused his servants and told them to saddle his donkey. He told Isaac to prepare for a trip, and he, himself, cut enough wood to burn a large animal. He said that God wanted him to make a burnt sacrifice on Mount Moriah. They set off on the journey, which would take about three days. Abraham carried a knife, and one of the servants carried a fiery torch.

The travellers reached Mount Moriah and climbed up some distance. When Abraham saw the altar not far away, he called a halt. To the two servants, he said, "Wait here with the donkey while my son and I go further up to the altar and worship. Tie the wood onto Isaac's back. Give me the torch." Motioning

God decided to test Abraham.

Isaac forward with the knife, Abraham started out again.

"Father," said Isaac, "you have forgotten a lamb for the sacrifice."

"Do not worry, my son," answered Abraham. "God will provide the sacrifice."

When they reached the altar, Abraham untied the wood and spread it on the altar. But instead of looking around for an animal to sacrifice, he motioned Isaac to lie down on the altar. Very frightened, Isaac did so. He lay perfectly still while his father tied him tightly to the wood and the altar.

Abraham picked up the large knife from the stones that supported the propped-up torch. Drawing a deep breath, he walked steadily to the altar. With the knife held in his fist, he draw back his arm. Just as he was about to plunge the knife into Isaac's heart, God sent His angel to hold back Abraham's wrist.

"Now God knows you are truly obedient

An angel held back Abraham's wrist.

and love Him above everyone else," said the angel. "Untie Isaac and live in happiness with a great reward to come."

Just as Abraham had finished untying Isaac and was embracing him, they heard a sound behind them. They turned to see a ram struggling to free his horns from thick, woody bushes where he was caught.

"The Lord has provided!" shouted Abraham with a joyous laugh. He and Isaac quickly caught the ram and tied it where Isaac had lain. Then very solemnly Abraham and Isaac made a burnt offering to God.

God's reward to Abraham was a promise that his descendants would be abundantly blessed and as numerous as the stars in the sky. This was indeed a great reward for a man who had great faith.

The Lord has provided!" shouted Abraham.

"The people of Sodom are evil."

A Pillar of Salt

The Jordan Valley was one of the most beautiful spots on all the earth. "The garden of the Lord," people called it. Birds sang in the olive trees, fish leaped in the sparkling river, and vines bent low with sweet grapes. Amid all this beauty were two wicked cities, Sodom and Gomorrah. The Lord watched with great sadness as the people there lied and cheated and stole from one another every day.

God went to his faithful servant Abraham and said, "The people of Sodom and Gomorrah are very evil. I will send my angels to destroy the cities."

Now Abraham had a nephew, Lot, who lived in Sodom. Abraham knew Lot loved the Lord, that he lived a good life in spite of the evil that was all around him.

"Lord," Abraham asked, "will you destroy the city if you find fifty good people there?"

And the Lord answered, "No, I will not destroy Sodom if I find fifty good people."

Abraham continued. "Do not be angry with me, O Lord, but what if there are forty good people, or thirty, or only twenty? Will you destroy the city then?"

God told his servant, "No, if I find even ten good people there, I will not destroy it."

So the Lord sent his angels to Sodom. It was evening, and Lot was sitting by the city gate when he saw two strangers walking up the dusty road. Lot bowed to the men. "Welcome, strangers. Kindly be my guests tonight."

The angels answered, "No, good sir, we have sleeping mats. We will spend the night in the town square."

Lot met the two strangers by the city gates.

But Lot begged them. "Please come home with me. Sodom is a dangerous place for strangers. I have plenty of food and drink, enough to share."

So the men went to Lot's house. They washed and ate, and as they prepared for bed, strange noises sounded in the street outside. It was the greedy evil men of Sodom, young and old, from every part of the city.

"Come out, handsome visitors! We want to see you. Lot, where are your guests? They look so interesting! Send them out so that we can meet them!"

Lot went outside and locked the door behind him. "Men of Sodom, I know the evil things you plan to do to my guests. Please, I beg you, do not harm these visitors."

But the men would not listen. They pushed Lot aside and tried to break down the door. The angels pulled Lot inside and blinded the wicked men gathered outside the house. It was then that Lot knew his visitors

The men of Sodom besieged Lot's house.

were from the Lord.

"You must leave this wicked city at once." the angels said. "The Lord has sent us to destroy it. Take your family and run for your lives. Do not stop or look back. If you do, you also will be destroyed with the city."

So Lot, his wife, and his two daughters ran up the valley, and flames of fire rained down on Sodom and Gomorrah. Lot could feel the heat from the burning city behind him. "Run, my wife and my daughters, run! Do not look back. The Lord will watch over us on the mountain."

But Lot's wife cried bitter tears as she thought of her house and her belongings burning up in the fire. She had to have just one last look, so she turned her head. In an instant, she became a pillar of salt!

Lot and his daughters made it safely up the mountain, where they found Abraham waiting for them. Down in the valley, nothing remained of Sodom and Gomorrah but

In an instant Lot's wife became a pillar of salt.

ashes. And there, by the side of the road, stood a tall rock made of solid salt.

Nothing remained of Sodom and Gomorrah.

The twins were different from each other.

Brother Against Brother

Isaac married Rebecca, but they had no children for a long time. Finally twin sons were born to them. The elder one was named Esau, which means "hairy." The younger twin was named "Jacob," which means "to take someone else's place." These names described both boys exactly. Red hair covered Esau's body. When Jacob was born, he was holding onto Esau's heel as if to pull him back so he, Jacob, could take his place and be born first.

The twins continued to be different from each other as they grew up. Esau loved the outdoors and became known for his hunting. Jacob liked to stay at home and was quiet and thoughtful. Their parents each had a favorite. Because Isaac loved spicy meat dishes, he favored Esau, who brought home meat from the hunt that was cooked into delicious meals. Rebecca's favorite was Jacob, who was at home all the time and who even helped her in her daily tasks.

As the first son, Esau was entitled to two things from his father: one, the birthright that belongs to the oldest son in every family, and two, Isaac's blessing. Jacob was full of envy that these two rights belonged to Esau just because he was born first. So Jacob plotted.

Jacob did not have long to wait before he saw a chance to get the better of Esau. As usual Esau had been hunting. This time, however, he stayed out too long and was exhausted by the time he dragged himself and his animal trophies home. He found Jacob cooking some soup.

"Will you give me your birthright?"

"My brother, I'm faint with hunger," said Esau. "Quick, give me some of your soup! It smells so good. "

Seeing his chance, Jacob asked, "What will you give me in return?"

"Anything, " said Esau. "The hunt took me so far that I haven't eaten in days."

"Will you give me your birthright?" said Jacob, dishing up a steaming bowl of soup but holding it just out of Esau's reach.

"Yes, yes," gasped the desperate Esau. "What good is my birthright if I'm dead from hunger?"

Jacob made his brother swear an oath to give Jacob his birthright. Then Jacob put the soup on the table and Esau ate hungrily .

In time Isaac, the twins' father, grew very old and was near death. His eyesight was almost gone. There was one important matter that Isaac had to attend to before he died. He had to give his blessing to his first-born son.

In a feeble voice he spoke to Esau. "My

"You must dress in Esau's clothes!"

first-born son, Esau, the time has come for me to bless you. Before I do that, let me have the pleasure once again of eating a dish of spicy meat, fresh from the hunt. This may be the last time you will provide such a treat for me."

Esau left immediately for the fields, intent on bringing down a fat animal for his father's meal . But, at the same time, Rebecca hurried to find Jacob, because she overheard what Isaac had said.

"Jacob, my dear son," said Rebecca to her favorite, "quickly kill two young goats from our flock so I can make a spicy meat dish for your father. Then you must dress in Esau's clothes, take the food to your father, and receive the blessing he intends to give his first-born son. Hurry!

Jacob ran to do as his mother ordered. Soon the steaming food was ready and Jacob was dressed in his borrowed clothes.

"Wait, mother," said Jacob. "Suppose my

"Come closer, my son!"

father hugs me as he gives me the blessing. Though his eyes cannot tell him I am Jacob, he will feel my hairless arms and know I am not Esau. He may curse me instead of bless me."

"You are right," agreed Rebecca. "So take the two goat skins and wrap yourself in them. They are just as hairy as Esau."

Old Isaac was a little surprised at how quickly his orders had been carried out, but he ate his meat with good appetite.

"Give me the blessing, now, father, that is due your firstborn son," said Jacob anxiously. He was afraid that Esau would return from the hunt and expose the plot if he didn't hurry matters along.

"You sound like Jacob," said Isaac. "Am I really talking to Esau, my first-born son?" The old man strained his almost blind eyes to see. "Come closer," he demanded.

Isaac was propped up on a couch and Jacob sat down beside him. Isaac sniffed at

Isaac formally blessed Jacob.

Jacob's blouse and smiled when he recognized the clean, fresh-air smell that Esau's clothes always carried. Next Isaac put his hands up as best he could and embraced Jacob. He felt the hairy goatskins on Jacob's arms and smiled again. "Yes, " he said, now satisfied, "you are my first-born, Esau."

Without wasting more time, Isaac formally blessed Jacob, making him the next head of the whole family, just as he had been blessed by his father, Abraham.

When Esau returned from the hunt, he found out about the terrible crime that had been committed against him by his twin brother. Furious, he swore to kill Jacob as soon as their father was dead. Rebecca did not want to see Jacob killed so she told her husband that Jacob should be sent to live with her brother Laban for a while.

"Jacob is looking for a wife among women we would not want to have for daughters-in-laws," Rebecca said to Isaac. "My brother

Esau swore to kill Jacob.

will see that he picks a suitable young woman."

Isaac agreed, of course, and the twins were separated. Jacob went 400 miles away, and lived and worked with his uncle Laban for a long time.

Many years later the twins met again and made peace with one another.

Jacob went to his Uncle Laban.

"Marry one of my brother's daughters."

A Trickster Learns his Lesson

"Listen, my son. Your brother Esau is angry that you tricked him. He wants to kill you! You must leave at once. Go to your Uncle Laban in Haran until your brother is angry no more." Rebecca helped her favorite son, Jacob, pack some food for his long journey. Jacob was ready to leave when his father, Isaac, called to him.

"Jacob, even though you lied to me, I love you, my son. It is not good for you to marry a woman of this place. Marry one of your Uncle Laban's daughters. Then God Almighty will bless you and give you many children."

BIBLE STORIES

Sorrowfully, Jacob kissed his parents good-bye. He did not know if he would ever see them again. His heart was troubled as he began his dangerous journey. Would God bless someone who had tricked his brother and lied to his father?

The trip to Haran was long and full of difficulties, but after many days Jacob neared the home of his uncle. The fields were dotted with sheep, for Laban was a wealthy man. Jacob called to some shepherds nearby, "Do you know my uncle, Laban? Is he well?"

The shepherds answered, "He is well. Look, his daughter Rachel comes now to water the sheep."

Jacob saw a beautiful young woman struggling to roll the stone away from the mouth of a well. He ran to the well and pushed the stone away for her.

"I am Jacob," he told the young woman. "My mother, Rebecca, is your father's sister. I bring you greetings from my family, Cousin Rachel."

Jacob saw a beautiful woman.

Rachel ran home and returned with her father. When Laban saw his nephew, he kissed him and brought him home to live. For a month Jacob worked hard, caring for Laban's sheep. At last Laban said, "It is not right that you work for me without pay. What shall I pay you?"

Now Laban had two daughters, Rachel, and her older sister, Leah. Jacob had loved Rachel ever since he had first seen her watering the flocks. "Let me marry Rachel," Jacob said, "and I will work for you for seven years."

Laban agreed, and Jacob tended his sheep for seven long years. The flocks grew healthy and strong, and increased in number under Jacob's watchful eye. For the first time, the young man who had tricked his brother Esau to gain wealth, worked hard to win what he wanted—Rachel.

At last the years of waiting were over, and Laban gave a great feast, with many guests, fine food, and wine. Jacob went to the wed-

Jacob tended his sheep for seven long years.

ding tent and waited for his new bride, Rachel, to come to him. But in the dark of the night, Laban brought Leah to Jacob instead of Rachel. In the morning, Jacob discovered that he had been tricked. "What have you done to me?" he shouted at Laban. "Why did you trick me?"

Laban answered, "In this country, the older daughter must marry first. Stay with Leah now and then I will let you marry Rachel also. But you will have to work for me another seven years."

Jacob was furious. How could his uncle cheat him this way? At last he understood how it felt to be tricked. The Lord must be teaching me, he thought. He agreed to serve another seven years, so Laban gave a second feast for the marriage of his daughter Rachel.

During the fourteen years that Jacob stayed in Haran, the Lord blessed him with many children and large flocks. He became a rich man, and one who learned to trust the

"What have you done to me?"

Lord. At last, Jacob returned home. He discovered that his brother Esau had forgiven him for the terrible trick he had pulled so many years ago. The two brothers and their families lived together in peace.

Esau had forgiven Jacob.

Jacob gave Joseph a coat of many colors.

Love and Hatred in a Family

At the age of 17 Joseph found himself in an odd position. He was both the most loved person in his family and the most hated. His father, Jacob adored him. Joseph's brothers hated him just because their father loved him best.

Jacob's love for Joseph showed in his eyes, in the way they shone when he saw Joseph. Jacob's voice was always very tender when he spoke to Joseph. The final proof of Jacob's love was a special coat he had made for Joseph, a coat of many colors. Joseph's brothers did not receive coats like it.

Joseph himself increased his brothers' jealousy. He had dreams, which he told his family. In one dream all Jacob's sons had been tying up long stalks of wheat. These bundles, called "sheaves," were lying in a field waiting to be picked up and stored in the barn.

"I dreamed last night," said Joseph to his brothers, "that my sheaf suddenly stood straight up. And then all your sheaves made a circle around mine and bowed to mine." The older boys understood this dream to mean that some day they would bow to Joseph as someone greater than themselves. This idea made them furious.

In another dream Joseph saw the sun, moon and stars bowing to him. This even irritated his loving father a little.

Jacob said, "Do you think your mother and I will be in your power? That is who you meant by the sun and moon, didn't you?" And, of course, Joseph's brothers got angry

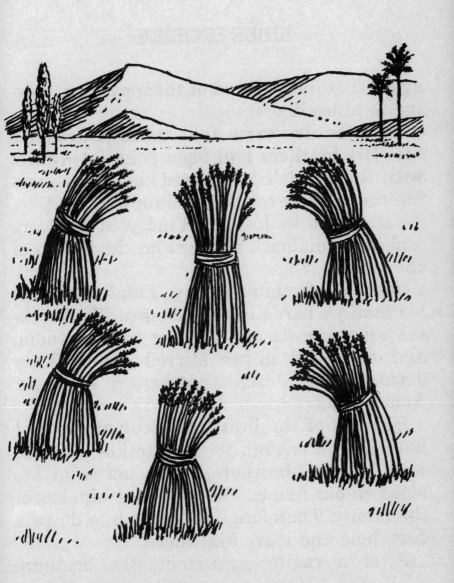

Someday they would bow to Joseph too.

again that he dreamed of them as stars bowing to himself.

Now the day came that changed Joseph's life. His brothers had been gone for awhile with the family's large herds of goats, grazing them wherever the feeding was good.

Jacob said to Joseph, "Find your brothers and bring me back a report on the health of the herds."

Joseph left immediately. Finally he saw his family's herds in the distance. His brothers also saw Joseph coming toward them, and their old anger stirred again. They decided to kill Joseph, out here in fields far from home.

But one of the brothers, Reuben, did not hate Joseph enough to want to kill him. He said, "No, my brothers, we do not want his blood on our hands. We only want him out of the family. Therefore, let us put him down a deep hole and leave him there."

After a raging argument, the brothers

Their old anger stirred again.

voted that Reuben was right. The hole would be best. The result would be the same for them but they would not have to actually kill their brother. Reuben was glad to hear this decision because he planned to come back alone later and rescue Joseph from the hole.

When Joseph reached his brothers, all their plans were made. They had even found a hole. They tore off the colorful coat that their father had given to Joseph. They dumped Joseph into the hole. Pleased with themselves, they sat down to eat.

As Joseph's brothers ate, they enjoyed watching the travellers on the road near them. Most people on the road were traders, with lines of helpers and camels, heading for Egypt. Some of the helpers were slaves.

One of the brothers suddenly said, "We can do better with Joseph. As Reuben reminded us, we are all the same flesh. So let us not be responsible for harming him even indirectly. After all, he may starve there or a

They dumped Joseph into the hole.

wild animal may attack him. Instead, we will *sell* him!"

There were shouts of approval at this brilliant idea. A trader would pay a big sum for a strong slave like Joseph. And they would all be innocent of causing Joseph's death.

Reuben was sent at once to get Joseph from the hole. But Reuben ran back to them, white-faced, eyes big. "He's gone! The hole is empty!"

Bitter at having cheated themselves of a profit, the brothers did not know what had happened. Then they overheard a trader boasting to some others who had stopped to eat.

"Today I am a very lucky man," said this trader. "I found a healthy young boy in a hole not far from here. I went to a lot of trouble pulling him out. But it was worth it. I stopped a wealthy merchant with many camels and slaves, who was on his way to trade in Egypt. He gave me 20 pieces of silver for this boy. Think of it, 20 pieces of sil-

"I found a healthy young boy."

ver for something I just happened to find!"

It was time for Joseph's brothers to return home with their goats—and without either Joseph or 20 pieces of silver. They worried about explaining Joseph's absence to their father. Then one of them remembered Joseph's coat of many colors and told the others his idea.

Again Reuben was sent on an errand. This time he was successful, for he found Joseph's coat that they had torn off him. When Reuben returned with the coat, the other brothers killed a young goat. They tore the coat more and dipped it in the blood of the dead goat.

When the brothers reached home, they gave Joseph's bloody, torn coat to Jacob.

"This is my Joseph's coat," gasped Jacob. "What has happened to him?" With solemn faces his sons told him Joseph had been killed by a wild animal. Jacob cried and cried for Joseph, and no one could comfort him.

Jacob said, "I will mourn my son Joseph all my life."

"I will mourn for Joseph all my life."

Joseph spent wisely and managed well.

From Rags to Riches

When the trader who bought Joseph reached Egypt, he put him up for sale in the marketplace. Immediately Joseph was bought by Potiphar, an officer of Pharaoh. Potiphar was rich, with a big household.

Gradually Joseph made himself more and more useful in Potiphar's mansion. Soon Potiphar saw that Joseph was capable of running the mansion and put him in charge of all the servants and all the household money.

Joseph spent wisely and managed very well. Soon the only decision Potiphar had to make at home was what he felt like eating

that day. The days in the mansion als
became more interesting for Potiphar's wif
because she was attracted to young Joseph

Joseph avoided his employer's wife a
much as possible. More than once he had t
say, "No, I will not betray my master." Bu
the woman was determined to have Josep
make love to her.

Finally, one fateful day, Potiphar's wif
cornered Joseph. She grabbed at him. H
pushed her roughly away. But she held on t
his loincloth and it came off. Joseph ran.

When Potiphar returned home, his wif
met him and held out Joseph's loincloth. "D
you recognize this garment?" she yelled. "I
belongs to this Hebrew you keep praising
Oh, yes he runs your houshold well, but no
he tries to run your wife too!"

Horrified, Potiphar ordered Joseph int
prison. But there Joseph impressed the hea
of the prison with his ability to organiz
everything and everybody around him just a

Potiphar's wife cornered Joseph.

he had impressed Potiphar. Soon Joseph wa
in charge of the other prisoners, and the
depended on him, too. He even interprete
their dreams when they had a troubled slee

Meanwhile there was trouble at the pala
of Pharaoh. Pharaoh had dreams that both
ered him, and no one could tell him wha
they meant. One dream had seven fat cow
eaten by seven thin ones. Someone tol
Pharaoh about Joseph's ability to interpr
dreams and he was sent for right away.

When Joseph heard Pharaoh's dream, h
said, "Egypt is about to have seven years
good harvests followed by seven years
famine."

By this time in his life, Joseph was in th
habit of advising everyone. So he continue
"It is clear what to do: store grain from th
good years so Egypt will not starve in th
years with no harvest."

Convinced—and impressed by Joseph-
Pharaoh selected him to follow the advice h

Joseph interpreted Pharaoh's dream.

had just given. Everyone in the palace
agreed with Pharaoh's decision, even though
Joseph was only thirty years old and had
just come from prison. Pharaoh was so con
vinced of Joseph's worth that he gave him
clothes fit for a prince, a special ring, a gold
chain, and a lovely, well-born wife, Asenath.

Joseph put his powers of organization to
work. He went all over Egypt, selecting
capable men to be in charge in each area.
Large storehouses were built and the grain
from the good years started to fill them.
Pharaoh had ordered that one-fifth of all the
grain grown in Egypt for seven years be put
in the care of Joseph's men, and so it was.

With the eighth year, the grain stopped
coming into the storehouses. There was either
no grain from a field or some tiny, mostly dis
eased kernels. Farmers had nothing to mar
ket. Soon they had eaten even their own
storage. Egyptians everywhere were begin
ning to starve. Now Joseph opened the

Pharaoh gave Joseph clothes fit for a prince.

immense storehouses and distributed their grain carefully to the hungry people.

People in other countries were also starving. In Joseph's home of Canaan, his father and brothers, along with their wives and children, were starving. But Jacob had heard the Egyptians had grain. Keeping his new favorite, Benjamin, at home, he sent his other sons to Egypt to buy grain from Pharaoh's assistant, whom everyone had heard about.

Admitted to Joseph's presence, his brothers did not recognize him. But Joseph knew them! He then began to play a little game with his brothers. He treated them roughly and questioned them about their home in Canaan. He pretended to doubt everything they said. Finally, he said, "Let this youngest brother Benjamin come here to Egypt as a sign of good faith."

The brothers were upset because their father kept Benjamin close beside him always. Jacob remembered he had lost

His brothers did not recognize him.

Joseph by letting him go with his older sons. But Joseph settled the matter by selling them grain and ordering Simeon, one of his older brothers, held as a hostage until his other brothers returned with Benjamin. He also had the money paid him by each brother put back in their grain sacks, without their knowledge.

Jacob was very upset when he heard what had happened to Simeon in Egypt. And he was confused—along with his sons—as to how their money could have got back into their sacks. He refused to let Benjamin go. Instead Jacob parceled out the Egyptian grain carefully to the many members of his family so it would last as long as possible.

But after some time, all the grain was eaten. Jacob then faced his problem: part from Benjamin or see his children and their families starve, including himself and Benjamin. He did the only thing he could do: he sent Benjamin with his other sons to Egypt

Simeon was held as hostage.

to buy more grain and redeem the hostage Simeon. He sent gifts and money for the new grain as well as the returned money from the first trip. Jacob said, "Getting the money back was an error some steward happened to make. It must go back."

Again on this visit Joseph played with his brothers. To their amazement he not only sold them grain but also gave a fine dinner for them. As they journeyed toward Canaan, however, the steward of Joseph's house followed and stopped them. He said, "My lord is missing his silver goblet. It is the one he drinks from and uses in making prophecies. Which of you has stolen it?"

All the men denied the theft, but the steward searched each pack and found the goblet in Benjamin's pack. All returned to Egypt. All were desperately frightened. Joseph received them sternly, but said they all might leave except the one who had stolen his goblet. "That one," ordered Joseph, "will

The goblet was found in Benjamin's pack.

become my slave here in Egypt."

But Joseph could not keep his pretense going. He suddenly sent everyone from the room except his brothers. Then he stood and spread his arms wide and said, "I am your brother Joseph. How is my father?"

It took some time before the men from Canaan could believe this miracle. But they knew it was Joseph when they saw the love with which he embraced Benjamin.

Now Joseph the Organizer took over. He sent his brothers home again, with wagons and orders to bring the entire family to Egypt. Almost seventy people moved from Canaan and were settled in an area near to Joseph. It was almost too much for Jacob for by now he was 130 years old.

But when Jacob saw his most beloved son, Joseph, returned to him, life flowed through his old veins. Jacob lived for 17 more years, a happy man. Joseph himself lived to be 110 and was much honored in his family.

"I am your brother Joseph."

The slave masters whipped the people cruelly.

Baby in a Basket

In the land of Egypt, the twelve sons of Jacob prospered, and they had many, many sons and daughters. Years passed, and each family became a great tribe. A new Pharaoh ruled Egypt. He feared these people, who worshipped the God of Abraham and Isaac. "Let us make the Hebrews work as slaves," he said, "so they will never take our land from us." The Egyptians forced the Hebrews to build their cities. The slave masters whipped the people cruelly, and worked many of them to death. But the harder the Hebrews worked, the stronger they became.

BIBLE STORIES

God blessed them with many children. The tribes grew and grew.

So Pharaoh passed another law. He ordered that all Hebrew baby boys be thrown into the Nile River. Some babies drowned and some were eaten by crocodiles. But one Hebrew mother thought of a way to save her precious son. She wove a basket of reeds and covered it with tar so water could not get inside. Carefully, she tucked her baby into the basket and floated it out into the river. "Lord," she prayed, "Pharaoh's daughter comes often to this spot to bathe. Guide the princess to my son, that he might live!"

"What a fine baby boy!" Pharaoh's daughter exclaimed, when her servants brought the basket up from the water. "I do not have the heart to drown this beautiful Hebrew child!" Instead, she took the baby to the palace and raised him as her own son.

The boy, named Moses, grew into a strong young man. One day he saw an Egyptian

"What a fine boy!"

master beating an elderly Hebrew slave. Out-raged that someone would whip such a feeble old man, Moses struck the slave master and killed him. Moses knew Pharaoh would pun-ish him, so he ran away and hid in the wilder-ness. There, he worked many years as a shepherd, but God had other plans.

"What is this?" Moses cried, as a bush at the side of the trail burst into flames.

"Moses," spoke a voice from the bush. "Go back to Egypt. Tell Pharaoh to let my people go." Moses knew it was the voice of the Lord. He knelt down, trembling with fear and excitement. God told Moses He had heard the cries of the Hebrew people and that, at last, He would bring them out of slavery.

Moses struck the slavemaster.

Moses stood before Pharoah.

To the Promised Land

Even though Moses had grown up in the palace of Pharaoh, he trembled as he stood before the ruler of Egypt, with only a shepherd's staff in his hand.

"Mighty Pharaoh, the God of Heaven and Earth says, 'Let my people go.'"

Pharaoh just laughed. "I do not fear your God. The Hebrew people are hard-working slaves. I will never let them go!

Then the Lord spoke to Moses, and told him to strike the waters of the river with his shepherd's staff. Instantly, all the water in Egypt turned to blood.

BIBLE STORIES

Pharaoh still laughed, "My magicians can perform that same trick. Get out of my sight, Moses!"

Following God's instructions, Moses went back before Pharaoh nine more times. Each time, he said to the Egyptian king, "The God of Israel says, 'Let my people go.'" Each time, Pharaoh laughed, so God sent terrible plagues upon the land. Frogs swarmed over fields and houses, gnats and flies stung people. All the cattle died, and locusts ate up the crops. Darkness covered the land, and the Egyptians suffered from sores all over their bodies. But Pharaoh would not let the Hebrew people go.

At last, God told Moses "This night, Pharaoh's heart will soften. This night, I will pass over Egypt. In each house, the eldest son will die, unless the door is marked with the blood of a lamb."

When the Egyptians woke and found their firstborn children dead, a terrible cry filled the land. The Hebrews fled, and no one

God sent terrible plagues upon the land.

stopped them. Freedom at last! Moses and the people sang for joy as they marched down to the shores of the Red Sea. But soon, Pharaoh changed his mind. He and his soldiers chased after the Hebrews.

Once again, God told Moses to use his shepherd's staff. As Moses lifted the stick, the waters of the sea flowed back, and a dry path opened. The people rushed across to the other side. Then God caused the waters to flow back, drowning all the Egyptians.

God showed his faithfulness and his mercy as he led the people. He fed them bread from heaven in the desert, and he showed them which way to go, even at night. God took Moses up to a mountaintop and gave him the laws by which his people were to live. In everything, God took care of the children of Israel, but they worried and complained. They wandered in the wilderness for forty years because they did not trust in Him. Finally, they reached the Promised Land.

A dry path opened.

Joshua sent two spies to Jericho.

The Fall of Jericho

After leading the Hebrew people out of Egypt, and guiding them in the wilderness for forty long years, Moses died. The Lord said to Joshua, "As I was with Moses, so I will be with you. You must lead these people so they can take the land I promised their fathers."

Joshua told all the leaders of the people to prepare to cross the Jordan River. "Get your supplies ready. In three days the Lord will help us capture this land." Then Joshua sent out two spies to look closely at the city of Jericho.

BIBLE STORIES

Inside the city, the men met a woman named Rahab. She hid them in her house when the king's guards came by. She gave them information about Jericho. In return, the Hebrew spies promised to protect her family when Joshua and his soldiers captured the city. Rahab tied a rope out of her window so the men could escape without being seen. They crossed back over the river to report to Joshua.

"Joshua, the people on the other side are very afraid of us." The spies said. They told him about Rahab. "Rahab says everyone in Jericho knows that the Lord is with us. She says the men in Jericho are afraid to fight us. Surely, the Lord has given us this land!"

It was a great day for the Hebrew people. After forty years of wandering in the wilderness, the Lord led them at last to the banks of the Jordan River. Over on the other side, the Promised Land, the land of milk and honey! With Joshua in the lead, the people

They had reached the promised land.

crossed over the river into the land that God so long ago had promised would be theirs. They stopped to worship and sing praises to the Lord. As Joshua finished his prayers, he looked up to see a man with a sword standing in front of him. "Are you a friend or an enemy?" Joshua asked.

"Neither," the man replied. "I have come to command the Lord's army. Take off your sandals. The place where you are standing is holy."

Joshua realized this man was an angel sent from God. "Does the Lord have a command for me, his servant?" he asked.

The angel told him that the Hebrew people were to capture and destroy the great walled city of Jericho. "Joshua, gather all your fighting men. At the front, place priests carrying trumpets. March around Jericho one time every day. Do this for six days. On the seventh day, march around the city seven times. On that day, the priests will blow the

"Are you a friend or an enemy?"

trumpets, the men will shout, and the walls of Jericho will fall!"

Early the next morning, the Hebrew soldiers lined up behind the priests. Silently, they marched outside the city. Tramp, tramp, tramp. Inside the walls, the people of Jericho were puzzled. Why did these strange soldiers march without making a sound? Tramp, tramp, tramp. The people grew more nervous. Were these men going to attack? The king of Jericho ordered the gates closed and placed more guards around the city. Tramp, tramp, tramp. Six days of silent marching passed, and each day the people of Jericho became more worried.

The seventh day dawned. The Hebrew soldiers were ready to march at the first gleam of sunlight. Around Jericho six times they marched. Tramp, tramp, tramp! The seventh time around, Joshua cried, "Shout, men, shout! For the Lord has given us this city!"

The men stood and shouted with all their

The soldiers lined up behind the priests.

might. The priests blew their trumpets until they had no breath left, and the thick stone walls of the city of Jericho crumbled like a clay pot. Inside, people screamed and ran, leaving everything behind them. Rahab, the woman who had helped the spies was right. Most of the men of Jericho did not stay to fight. The Hebrews followed, and easily defeated the few who remained.

The Lord ordered Joshua and his men to burn everything in the city of Jericho. Only things made of silver, gold, bronze, or iron were saved as gifts to God. Of all the people in Jericho, only Rahab and her family were allowed to live, because of the help she gave Joshua's spies.

The walls came tumbling down.

With his bare hands Samson killed the lion.

Strength from the Lord

A strong young man rested his head in the lap of a beautiful woman.

"Oh, Samson," murmured Delilah as she stroked his long hair. "You have the strength of ten men in your arms. Prove that you love me, and reveal the secret of your strength."

At this time, a foreign people, the Philistines, ruled the land of Israel. They were cruel, and did not honor God. But God blessed Israel with a hero, a man strong in the power of the Lord. Once, a lion attacked Samson. With his bare hands, Samson tore the lion apart. Later, Samson tied torches to three hundred foxes' tails and drove them through the Philistines' fields. The crops burned to the ground. In battle, Samson killed a thousand Philistine soldiers using just a bone he found in the hills.

So the Philistines wanted to capture Samson. They promised Delilah much silver if she could discover the secret of Samson's strength. Night after night, she kissed and begged. Samson told her lies about his strength so she would quit asking. Finally, he could stand it no longer. "Woman, I grow weary of your questions. My strength comes from the Lord. My long hair is a sign that I am faithful to Him. If anyone cuts my hair, I will become weak."

Samson fell asleep in Delilah's lap and she called in a man to shave off Samson's hair. When he woke, he did not know his strength had left him, and he tried to fight the Philistines. They gouged out his eyes and tied him up. In prison, his hair began to grow back.

"If anyone cuts my hair, I become weak!"

The Philistines gathered to celebrate. "Bring Samson out to amuse us," the king cried. They led Samson to the temple of their foreign god.

Samson prayed, "Lord, give me strength once more, so the Philistines can see the power of the one true God."

Samson pushed with all his might on the posts of the temple, and it fell, crushing the king and all the people inside. With his death, Samson killed more Philistines than when he was alive.

Samson pulled down the posts of the temple.

"I challenge your God."

The Boy and the Giant

Sunlight poured down on the beautiful hills of Elah. But when the men of Israel looked up, they saw a terrifying sight. There on the hilltop, a Philistine soldier stood shouting insults at them.

"You call yourselves the army of the living God. Then why do you hide in the valley? Today I challenge your God. Send out one soldier to fight against me. When I win, you will see that your God has no power. We will make you our slaves!"

The men who listened to these insults had fought many brave battles. But they feared this Philistine, for he was no ordinary soldier. Goliath stood nearly ten feet tall, and he wore a bronze helmet and a coat of mail. He had one spear tied to his back and held another one in his hand. Hundreds of men had died in battle, fighting against Goliath. Among all the soldiers of Israel, there was no man willing to fight this beast alone.

Only one person was brave enough to face Goliath—David, a young shepherd boy. He had come to the army camp to bring food for his older brothers who were soldiers.

David was amazed that everyone feared the giant Philistine. "Does Goliath think he can speak against the Lord? Let me fight this Philistine! When a bear attacked my father's sheep, I killed it. God saved me from the bear, and he will save me from Goliath."

Saul, the king of Israel, gave David a helmet, armor, and a sword. But David refused them. "I have never used a sword. I will take my slingshot and some stones from the

David was brave enough to face Goliath.

brook, and God will be with me."

Goliath roared with laughter when David stepped up to fight him. "What, do you send me a child? Come here, boy, and I'll feed you to the birds!"

The Philistine charged with his heavy sword, but the shepherd boy had his sling ready. Wh-r-r-r! A single stone flew through the air and struck Goliath on his forehead. The giant fell down dead!

The enemy soldiers watched in horror as David took Goliath's own sword and cut off their champion's head. The men of Israel charged up the hill and killed many Philistines that day. David became the leader of the army, and later was crowned king of Israel.

The giant fell down dead.

Solomon solved many problems.

The Wisest Man

It was midnight; young King Solomon tossed and turned on his bed. He had so many difficult decisions to make! All the people of Israel brought their problems to him. At last, Solomon fell asleep, and in a dream, God spoke to him.

"Solomon, I see you are troubled. Ask for anything, and I will give it to you."

Solomon's mind filled with visions of gold and jewels and great palaces and kings bowing before him. Should he ask for wealth or power or long life? Then the young king remembered the problems of his people.

"O Lord, you have placed me on the throne of Israel, but I am like a little child. I am not wise enough to rule your people. I ask, Lord, for wisdom, so that I might rule justly."

Solomon's answer pleased God. "Because you desire wisdom to rule my people, Solomon, you shall have it. Of all men to live on this earth, you shall be known as the wisest. And I will also bless you with wealth and power and a long life, as long as you walk in my ways."

In the morning the young king woke, strong in the power and wisdom of the Lord.

A servant knocked at his door. "O king, two women wish to see you. They have a baby boy with them, and each woman says the child is hers."

Solomon took his seat in the court. A woman threw herself at his feet. "King Solomon, this child is mine. That mother's baby died, and in the night, she stole my son. Now she says he belongs to her!"

"Each woman says the child is hers."

"Do not listen to her, O King!" the second woman cried. "This is my son. She is lying!" The sound of their arguments filled the courtroom.

Solomon looked at each woman. He looked at the tiny boy sleeping peacefully. At last the king turned to the guard standing by the throne. "Soldier, draw your sword. Cut the baby in half, and give a piece to each woman. That will stop this noisy quarreling."

The first woman just stared at the king, but the second woman screamed, "No, no! I beg you, King Solomon, do not hurt the child! I will give him to her if you will only let him live!"

Then King Solomon said to his guard, "Give the baby to the second woman. A true mother will suffer first before she lets her child suffer."

Word of Solomon's wisdom spread far and wide. People came to ask his advice, and scribes wrote down his wise teachings. The

"Cut the baby in half."

land of Israel became a great nation, and all who saw it said, "How great is the Lord, the God of Israel!"

Scribes wrote down his wise teachings.

"Find me a beautiful new Queen."

The Queen Who Saved Her People

Sparks of anger flashed from King Xerxes' eyes. "Because Queen Vashti has disobeyed me, she may never live at the palace again. Find me a beautiful new queen, one who will obey me."

Xerxes of Persia was a powerful ruler. He conquered Israel and brought many of the people to live in Persia. Mordecai was a Jew who worked in Xerxes' palace. When he heard that the king wanted a new queen, he thought of his young cousin, Esther. What a wonderful chance this would be for her!

Esther was very beautiful, so she was

chosen to live at the palace with several other girls. There, the young women were bathed with precious oils and dressed in fine gowns. Xerxes would pick one of them to be his new queen.

Mordecai told Esther goodbye. "May the Lord our God be with you, cousin, and tell no one of me or your family. There are those in the palace who do not love the Hebrew people."

The day came for Xerxes to choose his new queen. Esther's beautiful face and her soft pleasant manner pleased him. He placed the royal crown on her head and gave a great banquet in her honor.

Now the king's chief advisor, Haman, did not like Mordecai because he would not worship the king and the advisors as gods. Haman convinced King Xerxes to pass a law ordering the death of any person who would not bow before the throne. Haman knew that the Jews bowed only to their God.

When news of this law reached the people,

Xerxes chose Esther for his new queen.

a great cry rose in the land. Mordecai sent word to Queen Esther. "Ask the king to stop this evil plan, or all your people shall die."

Esther trembled with fear when she received the message. To go to the king when he had not called for her was against the law. To disobey meant death.

But she had to do something! For three days, Esther prayed. She took nothing to eat or drink.

At last, she put on her finest robes. She went to the king's inner courtyard and stood there silently. The minutes and the hours passed. Would Xerxes kill her when he saw her there? At last the king looked up. The sad look in his wife's beautiful eyes softened his heart.

"What is it, Esther? What do you wish of me?"

"Oh, King Xerxes, if I have pleased you, spare my life!" Esther cried.

The king looked puzzled. Esther revealed

"If I have pleased you spare my life."

her secret, that she was a Jew. She explained that she and Mordecai and all the Jews in Persia would die because of Haman's evil plan. Xerxes grew angry when he learned that Haman had tried to trick him. He changed the evil law and ordered Haman put to death. Esther's bravery had saved her people.

He ordered Haman put to death.

"O Lord, my God, save me!"

Daniel in the Lions' Den

Daniel sat on the edge of a jagged rock. It was so dark inside the cave, he could not see much around him. But the noises he heard were horrible—growls and roars and rumblings. Daniel knew those were the sounds of hungry lions. He prayed, "O Lord my God, save me! Shut the lions' mouths so they will not harm me!"

Outside the cave, King Darius of Babylon called to his friend, "Daniel, may the God you serve protect you!"

Daniel's enemies smiled. They were sure their plan would work. In the morning there would be nothing left in the lions' den but a few bones.

Of all the king's most trusted men, Daniel was the wisest. He served the king faithfully and never cheated him like the other advisiors did. The wicked leaders knew if they could get rid of Daniel, they could cheat even more and grow richer.

So they went to the king, "Live forever, Darius! We know that all good gifts come from you. Therefore, no one should be allowed to ask for things from any god or from any man but you, O King."

Darius was pleased, "Yes, truly I am greater than other men or golden gods. Who can give greater gifts that I, King of all Babylon? If a person disobeys this law, he must die."

Daniel heard about the new law, but he still prayed to God three times each day, just as he had always done. The wicked advisiors knew he would do this, and went back to Darius.

"I am greater than other men or golden gods."

"We have caught Daniel asking for things from his God. Now he must be thrown to the lions. Will you obey your own law?"

"But Daniel prays to his living God. He asks for nothing from any man but me. He is my most faithful advisor." Darius was greatly saddened, but he had no choice. All night, he paced back and forth, worrying about Daniel in the lions' cave.

At sunrise, the king ordered his men to roll the stone away from the cave. He peered into the darkness, afraid of what he would see.

But Daniel called out to him. "Do not fear, King Darius! My God sent his angel and shut the lions' mouths! See, the beasts sleep around me."

Darius ordered that the wicked advisors be thrown into the cave. The lions awoke and tore their bodies to pieces. The king wrote a letter to all his people, "Daniel's God is the living God. He does great things in heaven and earth. God saved Daniel from the lions."

"See the beasts sleeping around me."

"Let us leave as soon as we can!"

The Man Who Ran From God

Jonah handed the captain of the ship his money. "Take me to the city of Tarshish," he said. "Let us leave as soon as we can."

Jonah did not tell the captain why he was in a hurry. It was because of the Lord. Jonah had promised he would do whatever God asked, so the Lord had told Jonah to preach in the evil city of Nineveh. But Jonah was afraid and decided not to keep his promise. Now he wanted to go to Tarshish, as far from Nineveh as he could go.

The captain was glad to have a passenger on board. He set sail for Tarshish right away.

But a great wind whipped up the sea and the ship rolled in the huge waves. The sailors were afraid. They looked around for Jonah. He was asleep!

"How can you sleep in this storm?" the sailors shouted. "Get up! Pray to your God so that he will save us."

So Jonah prayed. But still the wind howled and the waves crashed over the side of the ship. Then the sailors said to one another,"Let us throw lots to see who among us is the cause of this terrible storm."

Each man threw the sticks, and each time the answer was No. Finally, Jonah tossed the sticks. This time the answer was Yes. Jonah was the reason the wind was raging so.

"What have you done? Why is your God displeased with you?" the men asked.

"I am a Hebrew," Jonah answered. "I worship the God of Heaven and Earth. Throw me into the sea. I know it is my fault that this storm has come." As Jonah spoke, the waves grew bigger.

"Who caused this terrible storm?"

But the men did not want to harm Jonah. They cried out to the Lord, "God of Jonah, we see that you rule the land and the ocean. It must be that you want this man back." Then they picked up Jonah and threw him over the side of the ship.

At that moment, the wind stopped and the waves calmed down. The sailors saw God's power at work on the sea, and they began to worship him.

Now swimming beside the ship was a great whale. The Lord caused the whale to swallow Jonah, and there he stayed for three days and three nights.

It was dark, and it smelled bad inside the belly of the huge fish. Jonah feared he would die at any time. He prayed to God, "Lord, hear my voice and save me from death. When I make promises to you, I will keep them, O God."

At last, God spoke to the great fish. The whale spit Jonah out onto the shore.

The Lord caused the whale to swallow Jonah.

As Jonah lay weeping on the sand, the Lord once again called him to go to Nineveh. "Get up! Tell the people to stop their wrongdoing or I will destroy them."

This time, Jonah did what God wanted. The people of Nineveh heard Jonah preach and they turned toward the Lord. The king ordered a day of going without food and praying, so that God might change his mind about destroying the city. When God saw that the people had put their evil ways behind them, he did not punish them. An entire city was saved because Jonah finally kept his promise to the Lord.

Jonah lay weeping in the sand.

Mary and Joseph looked at the tiny infant.

A King is Born

A baby's cry broke the quiet in the dark stable. There with the sheep and the cows, Mary and Joseph looked in wonder at the tiny infant. What was ahead for this precious child? Would the world know this baby was the Son of God, the Savior of the World? Mary tucked the infant into a feed box lined with clean straw. Then she rested and thought about all that had happened. She remembered Gabriel, the angel who had brought her God's good news. "Hail, Mary," Gabriel had said. "The Lord is with you. You will have a child and his name shall be

Jesus. He will be called the Son of the Most High God, and he will rule forever." Mary had been puzzled by this message. She was not even married then. How could she have a child? But Gabriel's words had come true. Here was baby Jesus, sleeping peacefully in the manger.

Joseph got up and checked on their donkey. It had been a long hard trip from Nazareth to Bethlehem. It was the time of the census, when all men traveled back to their birthplace to be counted. Even though Mary's baby was about to be born, she had to go to Bethlehem with her new husband, Joseph. The road had been rough and the donkey's back was so hard for poor Mary. Joseph sighed and looked around at the stable. At least they were in a warm quiet place now. When they had reached Bethlehem, the inns were so crowded, there was no room anywhere for them. Mary had been in great pain. The baby was coming, so Joseph had

It had been a long hard trip to Bethlehem.

found this spot. Now he wondered. How could God let his Only Son, the King of Heaven, be born in a poor stable?

Suddenly, Joseph heard noises outside. Had someone come to bother Mary and the new baby? A man peered into the stable, then turned to others with him.

"This must be Christ, the Lord, our newborn King! He is sleeping in a manger, just as the angels said!" A group of shepherds carrying torches and lambs crowded into the stable. Quietly, they knelt down beside the baby.

Mary and Joseph listened in amazement as the shepherds told how angels had appeared to them in the sky outside Bethlehem. Later, wise men who had followed a star for thousands of miles also came to worship the newborn King. It was all coming true, everything Gabriel had told Mary and Joseph! God so loved the world, he was sending his Only Son to bring the Light of God to all people everywhere.

"This must be Christ, the Lord."

He was a strange young man, living in a cave.

A Time of Testing

From villages and towns all over Judea, people came to the desert to hear John the Baptist. He was a strange young man, living in a cave, eating insects and honey he had gathered in the wilderness. But love for God shone in his eyes, and his words made people look deep into their own hearts. "Repent," John cried out to them. "Turn away from your sin. The Kingdom of God is coming soon!"

Out in the desert, listening to John preach, many people wanted to change their lives. They wanted to live for God, so they asked John to baptize them in the Jordan River. "I baptize you with water to show that your hearts have changed," John said. "But someone is coming who will baptize with the Holy Spirit."

One day Jesus stepped out of the crowd and went to John who was standing in the river. He asked John to baptize him. "Why do you come to me?" John asked. "I am not worthy to carry your shoes! You should baptize me, Jesus."

Jesus quietly answered, "My Father in heaven has asked me to do this. Will you baptize me, John?"

John turned to the crowd standing along the riverbank. "Behold, the Lamb of God!" John announced. "He will take away the sins of the world." And he baptized Jesus.

When Jesus came up out of the water, a beautiful white light glimmered around his head, like a bird coming to perch on his shoulder. A voice from heaven spoke, "This is my Son and I love him. What he does pleases me."

A white light glimmered around his head.

People at the river that day were amazed. Who was this Jesus?

After his baptism, Jesus went deeper into the desert, to be alone for a time and to pray to God, his Father. For forty days and forty nights, Jesus prayed, and he ate nothing. His body grew very weak and he felt great pain.

Satan came to the desert to tempt Jesus, to offer him things that would ease his pain. "Oh, Jesus, you say you are the Son of God," Satan teased. "If that is true, turn the stones of this desert into bread. Then you will not be hungry anymore."

Jesus was starving, but he knew he must not listen to Satan. "It takes more than bread to give life, Evil One. A person lives on every word from God."

Next, Satan flew with Jesus to Jerusalem, to the roof of the Temple. They were so high above the ground that the people down below looked like tiny ants. "Jump off this roof and prove that God loves you," Satan

"Turn the stones into bread!"

said. "If he does, he will send his angels to catch you, so you will not smash on the ground."

Now Jesus knew that his Father loved him. He knew that he had been sent to earth for much more important things than this silly test. "The Scriptures say, 'Do not test God,'" Jesus told Satan.

Finally, Satan took Jesus to the top of a very high mountain. From this peak Jesus could see all the kingdoms of the world and all the great things in those kingdoms. It was a wonderful sight. Satan whispered in Jesus' ear, "Look at the riches and the power down there. I will give it all to you, Jesus. Just bow down and worship me. Forget what God wants you to do. Just serve me, and you can have the world."

Jesus shouted, "Go away, Satan! I will worship only God! I will serve only him! I will do his will!"

Satan's face twisted in great anger. He had

"Go away, Satan! I will worship only God."

failed to turn the Son away from the Father. He left Jesus on the mountaintop, too weak from hunger to climb down. Right away, angels came with food for Jesus. They cared for him until he felt strong again.

The time had come to return to his people. He had so much he wanted to tell them about God's love!

Angels came with food for Jesus.

"There is no more wine."

New Wine, New Beginnings

"Oh, what will I do? There is no more wine. Some of the guests have had none. Everyone will know we could not afford to buy enough for the wedding!" The father of the bridegroom looked as if he might cry.

Mary, Jesus' mother, reached out to pat her friend on the shoulder. Times were hard, and almost everyone in the village had money troubles. Still, it was too bad this lovely wedding party had to be spoiled because there was no more wine. Mary looked across the room to where Jesus sat, talking with his new friends. Disciples, he called them. Jesus had just spent time alone in the wilderness, and he had a new strong look about him. Could he somehow help the bridegroom's father?

Mary caught her son's eye and crossed the room.

"What is it, Mother?" Jesus asked.

"Son," she whispered, "They have no more wine."

Jesus looked at Mary. Finally he said, "Dear woman, it is not yet time to begin my Father's work." And he walked away.

But Mary knew her son. She knew he would help his friends on this special occasion. So she turned to the servants. "Do whatever he tells you to do."

In the corner were six empty water jars. Jesus said to the servants, "Fill each jar full of water." The jars were very large, and it took many buckets of water from the well to fill them up. At last the job was done.

Then Jesus said to the servants, "Take

"Fill each jar full of water."

some water from a jar and give it to th
bridegroom's father."

When the father took a sip from the cup,
huge smile crossed his face. He had plenty o
wine after all, and it was the best wine h
had ever tasted! Only the servants, Mar
and the disciples knew what had happened

The wedding party went on long into th
night. The guests were amazed at the won
derful wine the bridegroom's father served
The bride and the groom began their new
life together with much happiness. Fo
Jesus, this first quiet miracle was also a new
beginning. His time to do God's work o
earth had come.

He had plenty of wine after all.

Lazarus was dead.

Victory over Death

The sound of weeping filled the air. Lazarus was dead. Friends and neighbors gathered to comfort his sisters, Mary and Martha. This house was one of Jesus' favorite places to visit, for he loved Mary and Martha and Lazarus.

When Lazarus had become ill, the sisters had sent a message to their dear friend. They knew Jesus could heal their brother, just as he had healed so many other people. But two days passed and Jesus never came. Helplessly, Mary and Martha watched as Lazarus grew weaker and weaker, and finally died. They wrapped his body in strips of cloth and placed it in the cave that the village used as a tomb.

Four days passed. Martha heard that Jesus and his disciples were close by. She ran to meet them. "Oh, Jesus," she sobbed. "Lazarus died four days ago! If only you could have come to heal him when we sent for you!"

Jesus looked at his friend with pity and love in his eyes. "Do not weep, Martha. Anyone who believes in me will have life, even if he dies."

Soon, Mary joined her sister and fell at Jesus' feet, weeping. "Lord, if you had been here, my brother would not have died."

Gently, Jesus helped Mary up. "Show me where you buried him."

Together, the three friends walked to the cave where they had placed Lazarus' body. The disciples and the neighbors followed. At the sight of the tomb, the sisters began sobbing again. Jesus, too, felt great sorrow, and he cried with Mary and Martha.

"Show me where you buried him."

Then he turned to his disciples, "Move the stone away from the tomb."

"But Lord," Martha said, holding the men back. "It had already been four days. Surely, Lazarus' body will smell bad."

Jesus answered, "Martha, I tell you truly, if you have faith, you will see the glory of God."

Then Jesus looked to heaven. "Father, I thank you that you always hear me. And I thank you that now these people will see and believe that you have sent me."

The door to the tomb was open. In a loud voice, Jesus cried, "Lazarus, come out!"

No one in the crowd around the tomb moved. Could Jesus really bring a dead man back to life? Yes! Lazarus stood at the opening of the cave, the grave cloths still wrapped around his body. He was alive!

When people heard the news of this great miracle, many believed in Jesus. But the elders in Jerusalem were worried. "Jesus has become too powerful. He must die."

He was alive!

A wealthy man had two sons.

The Son Who Came Home Again

Everywhere that Jesus went, he told stories. Most people enjoyed hearing them, but only a few understood that the stories contained great lessons about God. Jesus told the disciples they needed an open heart to hear the truth in his stories.

A wealthy man had two sons. The younger son came to his father and said, "I know that someday when you die, I will get half of all your money. I do not want to wait until then for my share. Father, give me my half now so that I can enjoy spending money while I am still a young man."

The father granted his younger son's request. The son packed up all his belongings and moved to another country far from his home. He lived an exciting life, giving parties for his new friends, wearing fine clothes, and buying anything that he wanted. But before long, every bit of the money that his father had given him was gone.

Soon afterwards, a time of very dry weather came to the country where the younger son lived. Weeks went by and no rain fell. People who had food kept it for themselves. They would not sell it, except at a very high price. The younger son had no money to buy food, and his new friends left him. He was hungry, so he looked for work. The only job he found was feeding pigs for a farmer. It was hot messy work, not at all what the son enjoyed doing. But he was so hungry, he was willing to eat the scraps of food that the farmer put out for the pigs. No one gave him anything.

The only job he found was feeding pigs.

BIBLE STORIES

After several nights of going to bed on an empty stomach, the son thought to himself, "I have been very foolish to spend all my money having fun. I am here almost dying with hunger, while the servants at my father's house have plenty to eat. I will now go home to my father and ask to be a servant."

So that is what happened. The son returned to his own country. While he was still a long way from his father's house, his father saw him and ran out to greet him. As his father hugged and kissed him, the son said, "Father, I am not good enough to be treated like this. I was wrong to spend all your money. Let me be your servant."

But the father would not listen. He called to his servants, "Hurry! Bring the finest robe in the house, and a jewelled ring and sandals! My son is alive and has come home again! Prepare a feast so that we can celebrate!"

The older son was out working in the field when sounds of dancing reached his ears.

His father saw him and ran out to greet him.

"What is happening?" he asked one of the workers. The worker told him that his younger brother had come home and their father was celebrating. The older son grew very angry when he heard this, and would not go up to the house to see his brother. His father walked out to the field and begged him to come, but still the older son refused.

"Father, I have worked hard for you many years. I have always done whatever you asked of me. Not once did you give a feast in my honor. My brother runs off and spends your money on wild parties and fancy clothes. Then he comes home and you celebrate!"

"Son, son," the father sighed. "I am glad that you have always been here with me. Everything that I have is yours. But we have to celebrate today because your brother was lost to us and now he is found. He was dead, but now he is alive!"

Jesus told this story to show his followers how God wants us to come home to him, no

"He was dead, but now he is alive!"

matter what we have done. Like the father in this story, God is happy to welcome back a son who has made a mistake. Jesus also wanted us to see that sometimes good people act like the older brother. They should celebrate when a person like the younger son turns away from his wrong-doing.

Jesus told stories to his followers.

"Come to the hillside this afternoon."

Teachings from the Hillside

All over Galilee, people were talking about Jesus.

"Have you heard the new Teacher? He speaks about heaven as if he had been there!"

"My son saw him heal a blind man!"

"This Jesus is different from other teachers of the Law. I could listen to him all day!"

In the marketplace, at the well, over the dinner table, the name Jesus was on everyone's lips.

One day, the disciples went around to all the villages. "Come to the hillside this afternoon," they announced. "The Master will speak to us there." Families packed baskets of food, shopkeepers closed their doors, sick people begged friends to help them up the hill. Everyone wanted to hear Jesus!

It was beautiful and very cool up on the hillside. Birds sang and wild flowers nodded in the breeze. Children played in the grass while their parents sat and talked with neighbors, waiting for Jesus. At last, he and his disciples arrived. As they walked through the crowd to the top of the hill, Jesus' heart overflowed with love for these people. So much of God's beauty bloomed around them, and yet all they saw were their own cares and worries. What should he tell them?

"My brothers and sisters," Jesus said. "Be happy, for the kingdom of heaven belongs to you. If you are sad, God will comfort you. When you try hard to do what is right, God will fill you with happiness. When you work for peace, God calls you his children. If you

At last, Jesus and his disciples arrived.

are treated badly for doing good, God will give you the kingdom of heaven. So rejoice and be happy in the Lord."

The clouds overhead shifted in the sky and a bright patch of sunlight shone on the grass beside Jesus. "Do you see this sunlight?" Jesus asked the people. "You are like this. You are the light for other people. A mother does not hide her candle under a bowl. She sets it up so everyone in the house can see. Live so other people can see the good things you do. When they see your good light, they will praise God."

The sudden sound of two little boys fighting in the crowd stopped Jesus. He walked over to the boys and gently pulled them apart. "My sons," he said with a smile, "God does not want us to pay back one bad deed with another one. If someone slaps your cheek, turn the other cheek instead of hitting back. This way, we will live in peace with one another."

Jesus sent the boys back to their parents

Two little boys were fighting.

and continued. "Most of us love our neighbors. We know how to be kind to people who are kind to us. But I tell you, love your enemies. Pray for those who hurt you. Then you truly will be children of your Father in heaven."

People in the crowd looked at one another in amazement. Jesus used such simple things to show God's will, like sunlight, or boys fighting. It was so plain and clear to understand!

An older man spoke up, "Teacher, I am a poor man. I did not go to school, so I cannot say fancy words when I pray. Can you teach someone like me to pray?"

"God does not want fancy words," Jesus answered. "God knows the things you need even before you ask for them. Pray like this: Father in heaven, we will keep your name holy. We want to be part of your kingdom. Let your will be done here on earth like it is in heaven. Give us the food we need today.

Jesus used simple words.

Forgive us for our wrong-doings. Do not cause us to be tested, and save us from evil."

A man sat in the grass playing with the money bag tied to his belt. "Do not save up treasure here on earth," Jesus said to the man. "A thief can break into your house and steal your treasure. Instead, store your treasure in heaven. Put value on the things that money cannot buy, like loving God and helping other people. Do not worry about what you will eat or what you will wear." Jesus stopped a moment to watch some birds flying overhead. "Look at the birds. They do not plant grain or harvest it, but God feeds them just the same. And look at those lovely lilies in the field. Even a king cannot dress as grandly as they do! If God gives the lilies beautiful petals to wear, surely he will take care of you."

Jesus looked around at all the people sitting on the hillside. Did they understand his message? Did they know how much God loved each one of them?

"Look at the birds."

"How many of you are fathers?" Jesus asked the men. "If your son asked for bread to eat, would you give him a stone? Of course not. You know how to give good things to your son. Your heavenly Father is the same way. He knows how to give good things to those who ask him."

Jesus continued. "Fathers, would you build houses for your families on rock or on sand? A wise man builds on the rock, for when the rains come, the house will stand firm. Everyone who hears my words and obeys them is like that wise man. His house will not fall in the storm. But the foolish man builds on the sand. The first rain that comes knocks the house down.

The person who hears my words but does not obey them is like a man with a house built in the sand.

Drops of rain began to fall, and the people looked around in surprise. They had been listening to Jesus so intently, they had not

"A wise man builds on a rock."

noticed the dark clouds gathering in the sky. Some picked up their mats and baskets to go home, but many followed Jesus and the disciples down the hill to the house where they would spend the night. Some wanted a touch from Jesus' healing hands, others wanted to hear more from this Teacher who opened their hearts to God's love.

Many followed Jesus down the mountain.

Were they able to carry on God's work?

The Last Supper

Candlelight flickered in the upper room where the disciples ate and talked quietly. Jesus looked from face to face. How he loved these men! For almost three years they had traveled with him throughout the countryside, teaching people about God's love. Now they had come to Jerusalem, to celebrate the feast of the Passover and to worship at the Temple. Jesus sighed. Did these men understand anything ahead of them? Were they strong enough to carry on God's work?

Jesus picked up a loaf of bread and gave thanks for it. He spoke quietly and the disciples leaned forward to listen. "This bread is like my body. It will be broken for you."

Jesus tore the bread in half and handed it to the disciples. "Take this and eat it. In days to come, break bread among yourselves to remember me."

The disciples looked puzzled as they pulled off chunks of bread. What was Jesus talking about, breaking his body? And how could they ever forget him, this Master they loved so much?

Next, Jesus poured a cup of wine. He held it up before them. "This wine is like my blood. My blood will be spilled for the sins of the world. Drink of it, all of you."

He watched the disciples drink silently. Then Jesus said, "My children, I can be with you only a little while longer. And now I give you a new commandment, to love one another as I have loved you. Everyone will know you are my followers if you love each other."

Peter was worried. "Lord, where are you

"This is my blood."

going? What will happen to you? I want to go, too. I will follow you, no matter what!"

Jesus smiled at this rough, strong disciple, "Peter, Peter, where I am going now, you cannot follow. I go to prepare a place for you, and then I will come back. For a time you will be sad, but your sadness will turn to joy."

Jesus said these things so that his followers would begin to understand about his death and the resurrection. After a time of prayer, the men left the table. Some of the disciples went on with Jesus to a quiet garden. Others prepared for bed. But one man, Judas, went to the elders of Jerusalem and told them where they could find his master.

The end was coming.

Judas betrayed his master.

"Crucify him! Kill Jesus!"

He's Alive!

"Crucify him! Kill Jesus on a cross!" the people of Jerusalem screamed. "He claims to be the Son of God. Our Law says he must die!"

Pilate, the Roman ruler, sadly nodded to his soldiers. He knew Jesus had done nothing wrong. But he did not want to make the people angry. The soldiers whipped Jesus with a leather strap tipped in metal. Blood poured down his back, but he never cried out. Next, the soldiers rammed a crown of thorns on his head. "Hail, King of the Jews!" they laughed. Finally, they ordered Jesus to pick up the heavy wooden cross and carry it out of the city.

As Jesus staggered by, the people grew silent. Just one week ago, they had cheered this man. They had hoped he would be their new king and free Israel from the Roman rulers. Only a few people understood that Jesus came to be a different kind of king, the King of Heaven and Earth.

On a hill outside Jerusalem, soldiers nailed Jesus' feet and hands to the cross and raised it up. For hours, Jesus hung there, suffering in the hot sun. "If you are God's Son, save yourself!" someone in the crowd teased.

Jesus looked to the sky. "Father," he groaned, "Forgive them. They do not know what they are doing."

By late afternoon, black clouds had gathered and thunder rumbled. Jesus suddenly cried out in a loud voice, "It is finished! Father, I give you my spirit!" The earth shook and darkness filled the sky. Jesus was dead.

"Forgive them, father!"

BIBLE STORIES

Three days later, some women who had loved Jesus went to his tomb to wash his body and wrap it in grave cloths. There had been no time to do this on the day he died.

"What will we do?" one woman asked the others. "We have forgotten about the heavy stone over the door of the tomb. We cannot move it ourselves."

"Perhaps the guards posted there will help us," answered her friend.

But when the women reached the tomb, they were amazed. The guards were gone and the stone had been rolled away. Jesus' tomb was open, and a bright light shone all around.

"Oh, sisters! Someone has stolen Jesus' body! How could anyone do such a terrible thing!" cried one of the women.

Suddenly, a voice spoke out of the bright light. "Are you looking for Jesus? He is not here. He has risen from death, just as he promised. Go, tell the others!"

Jesus' tomb was empty.

That night, the disciples gathered in a secret room. They were afraid the elders would punish them for following Jesus. The women had told them that morning about finding the empty tomb, but the men did not believe their story. One disciple said, "I will not believe Jesus is alive unless I can touch the nail holes in his hands."

Then, standing there before them, was Jesus! "Peace be with you! I am alive. Touch me and believe!"

The men looked at one another and then back at Jesus. He was alive! Jesus had come back to life, just as he said he would! They laughed and cried and hugged and laughed some more. He was alive!

Jesus and his followers talked long into the night. The disciples had many questions for their Lord, and he opened their minds so they could understand God's plans.

"I had to die for the sins of the world," Jesus said. "And now I go to be with the

"I am alive. Touch and believe!"

Father. But I leave you with a task and a promise. Go tell people everywhere what I have taught you, and my Spirit will be with you always, even until the end of the world."

IGB-IGB/5926-4/2575